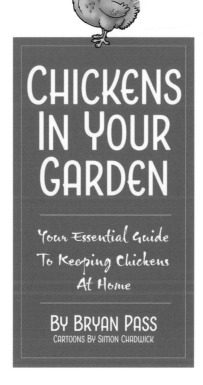

CHICKENS IN YOUR GARDEN

Your Essential Guide
To Keeping Chickens
At Home

BY BRYAN PASS

CARTOONS BY SIMON CHADWICK

Ceratopia Books, 2 Solent Road, Dibden Purlieu, SO45 4QG, UK

ISBN 978-1-9999045-4-8

First published by Ceratopia Books in 2018.

Text © 2018 Bryan Pass, illustrations © 2018 Simon Chadwick.   All rights reserved.

www.ceratopiabooks.co.uk

Contents

About the author

Being brought up on a New Forest smallholding, assisting with the feeding and cleaning out of a menagerie of animals before heading off to school each morning, was the foundation of a lifelong career working with animals for Bryan Pass.

Wishing to share their experience, Bryan and Dawn Pass opened up the gates of their New Forest farm as an educational unit in 1983.

Longdown Activity Farm offers a "hands-on experience" to thousands of schoolchildren and visitors every year, and is now one of the top visitor attractions in the New Forest.

Bryan has always been keen to encourage families to keep chickens in the garden, knowing just how much satisfaction these feathered friends can bring. From the excitement of finding the first egg the chicken's laid, to the daily duties of poo-picking and teaching the girls new tricks, he has shared his experience with many families encountering keeping chickens for the first time. Although he confesses that he is not clever enough to be a veterinary surgeon, he feels that his many years of experience and his passion for sharing his knowledge will be beneficial to anyone looking for down-to-earth help when considering keeping chickens in the garden.

First things first

The jungle fowl has been around for centuries and millions have been reared domestically either for egg production (35 million or so in the UK each year, although I have not counted them recently) or for meat to feed the masses.

This book is aimed at a very small percentage of people who wish to keep a few girls in their garden as pets and to be part of the family, to experience the real difference of eating fresh eggs compared with those that have been mass produced, often in an unnatural environment.

The number of small-scale poultry keepers is expanding dramatically as consumers are becoming increasingly concerned about how their food is produced.

There are many books and websites that will give you information on how to look after your girls, most of which are extremely informative and useful. The views and comments on the following pages are my personal experiences of looking after poultry. I am not claiming to be an expert, nor am I a vet; I am a farmer who has kept chickens all his life (which is quite a few years now) and who has gained satisfaction in supplying hundreds of families with their chickens and providing ongoing advice when required.

Most of the information available on the internet and in publications is based on traditional breeds of poultry. Personally, I rear hybrids, which have been bred solely for egg production. Their dietary requirements and husbandry needs differ from those of their old-fashioned cousins, so I sincerely hope that you benefit from using this book as a valuable source of information.

Are chickens really the pet you need?

Let's use this checklist to make sure you are ready to keep chickens as pets:

Do you have the space to keep chickens?

If you are looking for a pet to come into the house, forget it, you will not house-train a chicken. They will require a purpose-built house (coop) in the garden; each bird requires a minimum of 25cm sq sleeping area plus 3m sq of exercise area.

Are you legally allowed to keep poultry on your land?

Some local authorities do not allow any form of livestock to be kept on the land. It may be worth contacting your local Environmental Health Officer, and check the deeds to your property, as well. If you decide to keep more than 50 poultry birds of any species you will be required to go on the Poultry Register.

Have you discussed the possibility of keeping chickens with your neighbours?

It will be the neighbours who kick up a stink first if they do not like the idea of having chickens next door. They might complain to the local authorities about the noise or the smell. However, many enjoy having clucking neighbours and are kept happy with a supply of surplus eggs. In most cases it is best to pop next door and discuss the possibility of you keeping a few feathered friends, but may I suggest that you read this book first so you have the answers to any of the questions that they may throw at you.

Are you going to be a responsible chicken keeper?

The girls will need to be looked after seven days a week, depending on you for all their daily needs. Yes, of course, they will scratch about and find a small proportion of their daily dietary needs in their run, but the most important thing is that they are checked and cleaned out on a regular basis. They must have an early morning visit to let them out into the run or garden, top up food and water, have a quick health check and, most rewarding, harvest the freshly laid eggs. Again, as the sun goes down, make another quick check that all the girls are in bed and securely locked away.

Of course, you may spend hours just watching them scratching around during the day but I would estimate a total time of two-and-a-half hours a week to look after a small flock of girls. If you are planning a holiday or even just a night out you will need to have someone to take on these duties (payment in eggs is the norm).

Is anyone in the family allergic to feathers?

There seems to be a growing number of children and adults who suffer with various allergies. It would be an advantage to identify if this is going to be a problem before getting the chickens home, so a visit to a local petting farm or to friends who already keep poultry would be highly recommended, otherwise you may have problems rehoming them, as most suppliers are unable to take back poultry due to the high risk of cross contamination.

Do you really want them on your manicured garden?

A single chicken will (not may) destroy a well-manicured garden in minutes – just ask Dawn, my wife!

If you love your garden, keep the chickens off it. You will not be able to train them to scratch around the edges, they will quickly go to the newest plants and seedlings and hurl them across the lawn and path. As you shout at them, they will find more to destroy and happily cluck at you as you do a war dance, trying to persuade them to leave. If this is not bad enough, just imagine what damage they could do to your neighbour's garden, if they managed to find a gap in the fence. In a matter of a few minutes a beautiful, well-tended garden can resemble Twickenham rugby ground after a match on a very wet day. However, if you have a vegetable patch, a small group of laying chickens will harrow the ground extremely well in the autumn as they search for any remaining greenery and juicy insects.

It is always best to keep the girls off play areas and grassland where children are likely to play as their droppings can contain viruses, and their poo makes a sticky mess on the carpet.

Assuming that you have not been put off keeping chickens, the next step is to look at what is required before you bring the girls home.

Getting started

If you think that keeping chickens will help you save money, that is not really the case as the cost of setting up can be very expensive. However, the satisfaction of producing a regular supply of fresh eggs and having a hobby that can give the entire family hours of entertainment needs to be included in any calculations. Also, it's a great gift idea for the family which has everything!

Housing

Without doubt this can be the most expensive part of setting up but, before you scan through the eBay special offers, have a look around your own garden. Do you have a garden shed that is not being fully utilised? Is there a child's playhouse that is only used to store toys and garden furniture? I have even seen plastic compost bins being converted into useful coops, but be careful if you are tempted to use a disused rabbit hutch as these do not normally allow enough head room for the chickens. Maybe you have someone in the house who enjoys carpentry, although unless you can source your materials from a very cheap supplier, you may find it works out more expensive this way.

If all else fails then the internet is an ideal way of sourcing the coop, with many sites showing detailed photos of their 'improved designs'. I would suggest that you get what you pay for, and there are a few things that I would consider before parting with any money.

Personally, if I were starting with chickens, I would purchase a recycled plastic coop as these certainly reduce the risk of problems with red mite and lice, and are much easier to clean. Also they will maintain their value for several years compared with wooden. Admittedly it is quite a large investment but long-term it pays off.

There are a growing number of suppliers providing some very posh coops, but whether you want to go for the designer range or a cheaper version, it would be advisable to make sure you can see one before purchasing or check it out on a poultry forum.

1) The house should be large enough to home the number of birds that you intend to keep. It would be prudent to choose a larger house to accommodate a few more girls later on. An average hybrid chicken requires a minimum 25cm sq of floor space. It is worth checking the full dimensions when buying a coop as, for some reason, the recommended bird capacity is not particularly accurate on many of the imported coops.

2) If you do not want your girls to wreck the garden, then a coop with a run attached would cover the extra cost of replanting the flowerbed. Ideally, allow 3m sq per bird but 2m sq per bird will keep the animal welfare people happy. A shade on top of the run to protect them from the elements will be appreciated by the girls but, please, do not cover it completely as they do enjoy a little sunbathing at times.

3) Make sure you can access the house to clean it out (unless you are going to get the kids to crawl through the small entrance). It's worth making sure the doors have strong hinges and a secure fastener; there are some out there that a fox will easily open.

4) Nest boxes are best attached to the outside of the house, for ease of egg

collecting and they tend to keep cleaner. One box per four chickens is adequate, at least 45cm off the ground.

5) Plastic houses are much easier to clean and reduce the risk of parasites such as the dreaded red mite as there are no cracks or crevasses for them to hide in. However, it is extremely important that these are sited away from direct sunlight, to avoid the possibility of overheated oven-ready chickens.

5) Please do not buy a house with a felt top roof, as they provide a breeding place for thousands of red mites and even lice, which breed under the warm conditions and cannot be reached. Each night they crawl down and feed off the chickens and stagger back to their cosy environment and produce even more and, within a few weeks, you will have a major problem with your girls becoming lethargic and very poorly. Watch out when buying your coop online that the advert states what sort of roof materials are used; normally, if it's not mentioned, then you will most likely find it is felt, because it is the cheapest material to use, so do not be afraid to ask the question or you will almost certainly regret it at a later date.

6) A well-made wooden coop makes an attractive garden addition; some can be painted in pastel colours.

7) To protect the girls from predators, weld mesh should be used in preference over chicken wire, as you will find the crafty fox or badger will eventually get his teeth through the thin chicken wire to snatch his prey.

8) If there is a run attached to the coop, make sure the door is large enough for you to persuade the reluctant girls to go into the house, and that you can fit into the gap to retrieve the water container and feed bowl, otherwise you may be giving the neighbours something to laugh at as they watch you squeezing through the gaps.

9) If you are looking at a moveable house and run, it's worth checking that there are secure handles to allow you to move them, otherwise you will damage the framework.

10) If you are building your own coop, please remember:

- Ventilation is vital, with vents at the top of the house to avoid draughts. This will allow the ammonia to escape and ideally these should be adjustable to control air flow.
- Floor space: 25cm sq minimum per bird (hybrids).
- Outside run: 2m sq minimum per bird. This should be covered to prevent escapees and to keep wild birds out.
- Perches: 5cm x 5cm timbers rounded off on edges, 25cm off ground, allow 18cm per bird. Make them removable for ease of cleaning. If more than one perch, keep them 25cm apart.
- Pop hole door: 35cm high by 40cm wide.
- Nest boxes: allow one box per four chickens, 30cm by 30cm.
- Distance off floor: 15cm (ensure that they are lower than the perch).
- Nest boxes should be kept as dark as possible to avoid egg pecking; hanging a slitted dark cloth in front normally prevents this.
- Best not to site the coop in direct sunlight and consider drainage from the run.
- Please do not use felt on the roof!
- Set up the coop and fencing before bringing the girls home just in case it takes longer than you anticipated.

Fencing

If your girls are going to be allowed free range, to protect your garden and the neighbours', it's important that the perimeter fence is secure, mainly to stop predators from entering and also to prevent the girls from invading the gardens on the other side of the fence. Fencing panels are ideal for this or use weld mesh if there are dogs on the neighbours' side; a tough grade type is recommended and ideally should be dug into the ground about 30cm deep. Watch out for the clever chickens who, despite having their wings clipped, will still be able to somersault over a one-metre fence! Gates and doors will also require mesh of some sort; these feathered creatures are very inquisitive and will spend hours trying to find out what is on the other side of the fence.

Isolation pen

There are going to be times when you need to remove one or more of the birds out of the main coop. This could be because of bullying or illness or even a broody hen wanting its own space. Ideally a small coop should be situated close to the main coop to enable the girls to see each other; this could be a rabbit hutch or a brooder unit with a run attached.

Lockdown

There is always going to be a risk that wild birds will carry viruses as they travel from one continent to another and when this happens governments put restrictions on the movement of all poultry. The large poultry farmers will be informed directly by the regional authorities, however the small poultry keeper may not receive any direct notification of this. It would be advisable to join a local poultry Facebook page, which would send out notifications. Local media also put out information but this really depends on local interest. If you purchase your girls from a reputable supplier they should keep you informed of any restrictions.

Whilst planning your chicken area it is important that you make provisions for caging your birds in to restrict access of any wild birds mixing with your girls. This can be done fairly cheaply by purchasing some 19mm netting and securing it over the entire outdoor area to which they have access. Obviously you may have to restrict their foraging area when this applies.

We all know that these restrictions are a nuisance and cause a lot more work and sulky chickens whilst in place, however I plead with you to take all the recommended precautions to safeguard not only your girls but your neighbours and the farmers who make a living out of their chickens; when we all work together during situations like these we can soon get on top of any outbreaks.

What other equipment is needed?

As long as you provide a safe house to protect your girls from predators and provide food and water then there is not too much else that you require initially. As you get to know your girls you will find lots of things to spend your money on, if you wish to spoil them (no different than children).

Feed containers come in different shapes and sizes made from plastic or galvanised tin. The choice is yours and, depending on the depth of your pocket and your long-term intentions of poultry keeping, when deciding on which size to purchase it would be advisable that a full container should hold enough feed for all your birds for at least three days. Each hybrid chicken will eat approximately 150 grams a day. To avoid wastage, the feeder should have an anti-scratch insert around the base. Do not be tempted to use a bowl or biscuit tin as you will find that the girls will use this as a dust bath and have great delight in flicking all the Layers pellets across their run, until the last grain has disappeared into the dust. A weatherproof cover on top of the feeder is a good investment as this will allow you to place it in the outside run and not end up with soggy, compacted feed. It also allows more floor space for the girls inside their home.

Water containers are probably more important than the food containers. Chickens simply cannot digest their feed without water, therefore it is vital that

they have a supply of clean water close to the food station. Again, three days' supply should be available. An average hybrid will drink 450ml per day, however as this is where most bacteria and viruses will start from, I strongly recommend that fresh water is provided daily and the drinker is cleaned on a regular basis. If you provide water in an open bowl the girls will have fun scratching the dirt into this and within minutes it will resemble a pig's mud bath. Both feeder and drinker ideally should be extended 15cm-20cm off the ground to reduce the risk of contamination. Hang it from a chain or put it on top of blocks; there is no need to put weatherproof covers on the drinkers. Medication and tonics are normally given through the water, therefore it would help if there are quantity markers embedded on the side. If you are going to provide apple cider vinegar for your girls it would be best to provide this in a plastic water drinker as this will most likely corrode the galvanised ones.

Inside the coop

The type of bedding used inside the house is a personal choice. I enjoy watching the chickens scratch about in layers of straw; they do get a lot of satisfaction in spreading it around the house and searching for grain and insects. The disadvantage of this is that they also take it out into the run, which can create a soggy mess on a wet day. I have a large field where I can spread the end product but, if you have a small garden, it will require a good compost heap to dispose of it in.

Wood chippings on the floor and barley straw in the nest box makes an ideal compromise during the summer months, then perhaps put straw on the floor during the colder months to help keep the girls warm and active. There are varying opinions as to using hay or straw in the nest box. I have experienced some major lice problems when using hay, as this soon goes mouldy during wet periods, which then acts as an ideal breeding zone for the lice to expand in numbers. Also the girls tend to eat the hay, creating a risk of compacted crop. Barley straw is softer than wheat and oat varieties. If you purchase your straw in sealed plastic bags this will reduce the risk of bringing in red mite.

Wood chippings purchased in the larger bags are a more economical buy, but please remember that all bedding must be stored in a dry place.

Shredded paper can be used on the floor and in the nest box, but this can get wrapped around the girls' legs, causing them to panic, and it can get blown around. The use of shavings rather than wood chips is very often debated. Wood shavings are more absorbent, however, no matter what is written on the bag, it tends to be very dusty. Wood chips will last considerably longer and can be used in the outdoor run when they get wet. Both products will readily mulch down to produce excellent compost.

Cleaning materials

A strong shovel, paint scrapper, hand brush and a supply of strong plastic bags, plus a container of strong disinfectant and lots of elbow grease, is all that is required to keep your girls clean and healthy.

Depending on your coop, it is best to pick up the droppings under the perches daily and give the whole house a clean out once a week. Make sure that the soiled waste is moved well away from the chicken area and preferably somewhere that they do not have access to, otherwise all the creepy crawlies that you have just moved out will be heading back.

If there is a problem in the house with red mite or lice it's best to clean them out on a more regular basis. A full clean, which involves moving everything from the nest box, scrubbing down the perches and the interior walls, as well as the feeder and drinker, should be carried out at least once a month.

First aid kit and health box for chickens

As with all livestock it's best to be prepared and a box with a few essentials could save a trip to the local veterinary surgeon. Good housekeeping can prevent many problems; this list of goodies will put you in good stead to prevent problems and to deal with any minor ailments:

- 1 litre poultry house cleaner or disinfectant – for use in keeping the house clean and free of the little bugs

- 1kg Diatomaceous earth for spreading in the house to prevent a build-up of red mite

- 250ml Poultry Tonic or apple cider vinegar to add to their water when the girls go into a moult or are stressed

- 1 can of antiseptic spray for wounds

- 1 small pot of Vaseline (or Diprobase) for infected areas or feather loss; ideal for scaly legs and rubbing on to the combs during frosty weather to prevent frostbite

- Cotton wool – to clear weepy eyes and runny nostrils

- Egg box to carry all the eggs back to the kitchen

Food for your chickens

If you are looking for a regular supply of eggs from your girls it is important that you feed them well. Hybrid chickens have been bred to produce good-sized eggs as cheaply as possible. That is why they are smaller framed than their traditional predecessors. These girls will produce a 65 gram egg each day after consuming just 125 grams of feed. Well, that's what happens in the commercial world! With your girls having more exercise, they may burn off more energy and will fill themselves up with lots of juicy insects and flowers from the garden. The most important part of their daily diet, without doubt, is Layers pellets or Layers meal. All large commercial brands are suitable for the hybrids as long as they contain a minimum of 16% protein. If you wish to pay more for their food, there are some very good organic and GM-free feeds on the market, however I have found that sometimes these do not contain enough digestible proteins during the winter months, which sometimes prevents the girls continuing to lay throughout the winter.

It's great fun giving the girls scraps and tit-bits but please be careful not to spoil them too much otherwise they will simply stop laying. Scraps should not be fed to them until the afternoon. In theory they should have eaten 80% of their daily requirement by midday and this should provide enough to produce a tasty egg.

If you find they go off lay suddenly it would be advisable to stop all scraps and keep them confined to the run and coop for 10 days; this will bring them back into lay.

No matter how they look at you with pleading eyes, please do not feed your girls any meat or kitchen leftovers (this is against the law) as there is a risk of contaminating your girls with various diseases and viruses. Any crops grown in your own garden are fine.

Of course, your girls will love mixed corn as children love chocolate, but it can be extremely harmful if overfed. Wheat and barley contain only 10% protein and lots of energy, which will soon turn your trim-line girls into dumplings, and fat chickens are not very productive. You will soon find a drop in egg production if they are overfed. Another problem is that hybrid chickens have a much smaller digestive system than their traditional bred cousins and often too much grain will lead to compacted crop. If you really want to give them some corn, no more than a small egg cup full for each bird in the afternoon would be acceptable.

What plants are poisonous to chickens?

In general a well-fed chicken will not consume poisonous plants as most have a very bitter taste, however there are a few plants that I would remove from the garden to be on the safe side. These would include:

- Rhubarb
- Young potato sprouts and leaves
- Irises
- Ivy – mainly young shoots
- Privet

These are the ones that I have experienced causing a problem, however, if you keep your girls well fed with Layers pellets it will be just bad luck if they find a poisonous plant in your garden. I am more concerned about slug pellets, nitrates and chemicals used on lawns. Rodent bait that some poultry keepers scatter around can also be a problem. These are more palatable for the inquisitive girls and cause problems quickly.

Special treats

Like any pet we do like to spoil them at times with treats and it's fun watching their actions whilst eating them. Each bird has its particular favourites and it is part of the enjoyment in experimenting with different flavours. This is a short list of 'special treats', some that I would recommend and others that I would avoid.

The healthy list

- Bananas: A good potassium source, but one banana between three chickens, minus the skin, once a week, otherwise you could cause an imbalance in their potassium levels.

- Soft fruits: Ideal source of vitamins and it's great fun watching the girls running off with a strawberry or gooseberry in their beak, however too much and they will be runny from the tail end.

- Greens: All greens contain many minerals and vitamins. A cabbage tied up in the run will give endless hours of entertainment and help reduce boredom. Green potato skins and shoots can be toxic and are best avoided. Do not leave surplus on the floor of the chicken run otherwise this will attract rodents and wild birds.

- Dairy products: Yoghurts, milk mixed in with porridge, will help your girls get through very cold spells and aid quicker regrowth after a moult, but please be aware that all poultry struggle to digest dairy products so little and often is the best policy. Plain yoghurt would contain less sugar and therefore would be more beneficial. If you are having problems with soft shelled-eggs, whole milk will help increase availability of calcium in their digestive system. Mixing dairy products with Layers pellets or mash is ideal but please make sure that they have fresh every day otherwise you will create a bacteria build-up.

- Rice and pasta: If you want to get into your chickens' good books then boil up some rice or pasta and watch your girls dance as they squabble to dive on to these manmade worms! It will not make them too fat but please do not overfeed.

- Mealworms: Now you are talking. Dead or alive, these things will go down a treat and they are a perfect feed, high in protein, and enjoyed by all the girls. Please be careful not to feed too many each day as this can cause an imbalance in the protein intake. If they don't want mealworms then they are probably ill. If you need to get powdered medication into the girls, simply mix it into a few mealworms.

The current legal requirement of feeding mealworms to poultry in the UK states:

"Dried terrestrial invertebrates (insects) and processed animal proteins (PAPs) of insect origin cannot be used in farm animal feed or in treats, eg hen treats."

"Dried aquatic invertebrates can only be used in farm animal feed (for non-ruminants) if they come from an approved ABP premises (or non-EU equivalent) – then they're considered fishmeal."

I will leave the decision of feeding mealworms to you. Better still, why don't you set up a wormery using a composter and supply your girls with a daily treat of home-grown worms!

The not-so-good list:

- Meat: Please do not feed any meat or meat byproducts to chickens. It is against the law in England and rightly so, as this is a major source of bringing problems into your flock (and everyone else's). With meat being imported from all over the world there is a chance that some viruses will be lurking in the meat and no matter how well you cook it there is a strong possibility that viruses could survive and cause havoc to your chickens, then spread to others very quickly.

- White bread is a product that I am not keen on feeding to chickens. I know that most people get away with it but it seems that for some reason too much white bread does upset their digestive system and can lead to very mucky tail ends. Brown bread does not seem to have the same effect, but please do not give two or three girls a whole loaf, otherwise you will be asking for trouble.

- Chocolate should never be fed to your girls. OK, it will not rot their teeth but it would not take long to upset and eventually poison them. If you love your chocolate then eat it yourself. I promise that you are not going to produce chocolate flavoured eggs by ramming a Fruit and Nut bar down their throats.

- Onions are best avoided. The girls are unlikely to eat them, however if they got the taste of them it would probably affect their appetite for a few days whilst they clear it out of their system. Even though garlic is the same family, used in moderation it is definitely a perfect supplement.

- Alcohol and chickens do not go together although a small amount of stout in warm milk given to a poorly chicken can be accepted. The nicotine from cigarettes can quite easily kill them so please do not allow the chicken run to be used as a dumping ground for discarded cigarette butts.

Choosing your girls

Where do you go to buy your chickens? There is not a shortage of people selling chickens; in fact, as the demand increases so does the amount of suppliers. If you are a first-time buyer it's best to source a supplier who is going to give you advice and back-up when you get the girls home. You will undoubtedly have lots of questions to ask prior to buying the girls, and if things go wrong you will need to discuss with the supplier before spending out on vets. Without doubt the best way to source a local supplier is to talk to neighbours or friends who have chickens. They will soon tell you if their contacts are to be recommended or not. You will find adverts for breeders in local newspapers and websites, there are auctions that you could attend and various markets, however I would strongly recommend using an established outlet who will spend the time to discuss the health and welfare of your new girls.

Which breed?

There are thousands of breeds to choose from. Some pedigree stock carry designer price tags: the glamorous looking types, those laying green and blue eggs, the feathered leg varieties and the elegant hat-wearing types – you could fall in love with them all! Now let's get back to reality. What do you want from the chicken: admiration from the neighbours or a regular supply of eggs to feed the family? If it's the egg supply then you will need to look at the hybrids. These are birds that have been bred to simply produce eggs. Back in the 1950s, when there was a need to produce more eggs as cheaply as possible, different strains of chickens were matched up together to find the perfect egg-laying bird, one that would lay over 300 good-size eggs a year, not eat too much food, be small enough to put into a cage with a few more, and docile enough to avoid them fighting each other. This type of chicken comes with a guarantee of producing lots of eggs when given a loving home.

How much will the chickens cost?

There is a very large difference in the price of chickens. Again, the hybrids should be the cheapest with the very fancy breeds carrying an expensive price tag. The chickens that we sell at Longdown Activity Farm are hybrids. These come in all colours with fancy names but although all hybrids will provide you with a regular supply of eggs, do not expect to get a Sunday roast from them when they have finished laying. If you are looking for a traditional breed of bird then you will need to look for a specialist breeder; search engines or poultry Facebook pages are good for this.

A quick reference to different types of hybrid chickens

The rearing of hybrid chickens is a very large, competitive business. A huge amount of research has been undertaken by various companies to produce top quality stock for the commercial market and these companies keep their breeding programmes a very closely guarded secret. As a domestic keeper we really do not require too much information; as long as we are purchasing a female chicken that is going to produce enough good quality eggs to feed our families, and one that will live happily in our garden and convert the feed that we give them into eggs and not bananas, then that is all we really need to know. Of course, it would be nice to have some variety in colours and a chicken that likes to be handled. There are thousands of different names given to hybrid chickens. Some of these are very imaginative, just like the local real ales that I like to sample, but in reality they will all produce similar amounts of eggs because that is what they have been bred for.

The bog standard brown chickens, sometimes referred to as Warrens (Rhode Island Red x Plymouth Rock), are the brown-egg-laying machine. These, I would rate without doubt, as the easiest bird to look after and they are normally very docile, ideal for the novice keeper and as a child's pet. Producing six good-sized dark brown eggs a week on average during its first 15 months, this may drop to four or five eggs a week, but if fed well these girls will continue to lay eggs for about four years, although I have known some of these girls live to nine years.

Silver or white hybrids are exactly the same as the brown girls expect they come out white as the breeding has been reversed (Plymouth Rock x Rhode Island Reds). Again, they are ideal for the novice keeper who is looking for a regular supply of eggs, but these are not so popular with the commercial keepers because of the colour – the eggs are normally pale brown.

Most birds crossed with a Maran will have grey coloured feathers; some will be speckled while others will be a blueish colour. If you are looking for a very dark brown egg then these are the girls for you; any hybrid which has been crossed with a Maran will supply five dark brown eggs each week during its first 15 months, and these girls would most likely outlive the brown girls by a year or two.

Light Sussex (hybrid) chickens are normally a cross between the old fashioned Light Sussex and a Rhode Island Red. The very distinguished black markings around the neck and tail feathers make these girls very glamorous. They do like to be in charge of any other breed so very often they are a dominant and bossy bird, but they will supply an average of five light brown eggs a week in their first 15 laying months. These girls can live to a grand old age of 10 years but you will be paying their pension by then.

Rhode Rocks and Barred Rocks are the tough girls of the poultry world, crossed between the Rhode Island Red and Barred Plymouth Rock (reversed cross for the Barred Rock). They produce an average of five good sized brown eggs during the first 15 months of lay. Their eggs are normally harder shelled than most other breeds. I have found that these are less prone to 'scaly leg' due to their dark or black coloured scales on the legs. They are great foragers and efficient converters of garden waste into tasty eggs. Most of these will continue to lay for up to five years.

Now if you really want to be able to show off your girls, I would suggest that the most handsome hybrid on the market is the Bluebell – a French Maran crossed with Rhode Island Red. There are a few variations with companies trying to produce a heavier breed, and their plumage is very soft and extremely dense with various shades of grey. These girls will follow you around like lambs but I have found they are not so keen to be picked up and cuddled. They stand taller than most hybrids and make excellent foragers, so they will wreck your garden within minutes with their strong lanky legs. They should easily produce five large dark brown eggs a week in the first 15 months of laying. It's not uncommon for these girls to exceed six years, albeit the egg production will drop dramatically after five years.

If you are fed up with the normal brown coloured egg, then White Leghorns are the girls for you. The shells are bright white and extremely hard (even jackdaws struggle to crack them open). They will produce six eggs a week for the first 15 months, followed by five eggs a week for the next 15 months, but by then they will have burnt themselves out. I have found these to be a bit flighty and prefer to roost up in trees rather than in the coop. They are smaller than most other hybrids and very often will be picked on by the bullies. Their very white feathers are dazzling, though.

What to ask for when viewing chickens

You may be an expert or a novice, it really does not matter, but there are some facts that you need to know when you purchase your new girls:

What breed are they?

You should be told exactly what breed they are; if you are buying traditional breeds it's worth knowing who the original breeder was for future reference when choosing future breeding stock.

What age are they?

An ideal age to buy your girls is 16-20 weeks. These are classified as Point of Lay; it does not guarantee that they will lay when you get them home as that will depend on many other factors. Ideally you should purchase your girls two or three weeks before they come into lay as this allows them to become accustomed to their new environment. It is very unlikely that a chicken

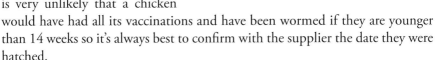

would have had all its vaccinations and have been wormed if they are younger than 14 weeks so it's always best to confirm with the supplier the date they were hatched.

Are they guaranteed females?

Assuming that you are buying your girls to lay eggs, then it would not make sense to buy a cock-bird. There is no advantage having a boy amongst the girls; in fact, it would cause more problems than it's worth. Chickens will produce eggs quite happily without any boys being present. Obviously they will not be fertile but the girls are normally friendlier without the presence of a male strutting about amongst them and no matter how nicely you speak to your young man he will still upset the neighbours at whichever time he chooses with his vocal outbursts.

Have they been fully inoculated and if so do you have a list of what with?

All commercial poultry rearers vaccinate their stock with a large number of different vaccines. These can be different depending on geographical circumstances. A rearer with thousands of young birds would not risk not vaccinating his flock as just one illness could jeopardise his business. However, many smaller producers do not worry about vaccinating their stock as it's difficult to buy the vaccines in smaller quantities. Personally I feel that it is better to be safe than sorry. Rearers are normally happy to give you a list of all vaccines that the girls have had. Please bear in mind that even if your girls have been vaccinated it is still possible for them to contract some of the viruses that go around.

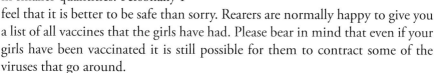

Have they been wormed and if so with what and when was the last wormer administered?

Most rearers will commence a worming programme when the girls are about 14 weeks old and treat them with a product called Flubenvet. There are others who prefer not to worm them in case the new owners prefer to use an organic product. It is advisable to check with your supplier and ask their advice on the frequency of worming.

What are they being fed on now?

Moving a chicken to a new home can be very stressful for the poor girls, therefore to change their feed at the same time is adding to the problem and can cause some major issues, so it's worth asking for a small bag of their current feed to reduce this risk or simply make sure you have the same type in stock.

Are they housed in deep litter or are they trained on perches?

Many rearers keep their chickens on deep litter, therefore the girls will not be used to using the perches in their new house. It's worth knowing this from the start as you then will know that you will need to lift them up on to the perches when it gets dark. This will help prevent them from sleeping in their nest boxes and spoiling the eggs.

Have they had their wing clipped?

To prevent the girls attempting to scale the neighbours' fence it's advisable to clip a wing. Don't clip both wings otherwise they will soon regrow and off she will go. Most rearers will happily show you how this is done; it is one of those jobs that is easy when you know how. If you are not letting your girls out in the garden or would prefer to let the girls fly up in the trees then there is no need to clip the wings, but even if that is the case then it would be best to have been shown in case your new friends decide to visit the neighbours' garden. Please do not take your chicken to a vet to clip its wing.

Do you offer a warranty on your chickens?

Would you consider buying a car or electrical appliance without a warranty? Chickens do not come with a three-year guarantee, however a reputable supplier should offer some form of assurance that if you have problems with your girls they will give you support. At Longdown Activity Farm all our livestock carry a 28-day warranty. If things go wrong for any health reason we will give support and advice. We cannot take chickens back to re-home due to our strict movement regulations, but our after-sales advice continues throughout the chicken's lifetime. Hopefully most reputable breeders will offer a similar service.

How do I tell if it's healthy?

Most rearers will let you choose your own girls so there are a few things that you need to consider when viewing them. If you are not happy with the girls do not be afraid to say so. You do not want to take home problems!

Watch the chickens walking. They should walk with their head up high and the tail facing upwards or at least straight. If its tail is tucked down this indicates a digestive problem. When they walk they should raise their legs elegantly and be weight bearing on both feet.

The comb and wattles should be a pink or reddish, depending on their age.

Do not be alarmed if the chickens do not want to be caught as this has probably happened before when they have been chased and injected. Crouch down in their area and let them come to you. Do not be tempted to go for the smallest or weakest as that will bring a costly veterinary bill with it.

With the young lady tucked firmly under your arm, check the nostrils are clean and free of mucus. The beak may be trimmed at the point (this is common practice for hybrid chickens); ideally the trim should be just noticeable and not halfway up its beak as this will restrict its ability to pick up insects. Listen to the breathing; if it sounds chesty or rattling, put it down. If you find another one similar say goodbye to the rearer (politely), as this would be an indication that there is a respiratory problem on the premises.

Feel the legs; they should be fairly smooth and they will vary in colour. Check the feet; toes are sometimes disjointed but make sure that there is not a build-up of dirt on them.

Gently pull back the feathers to check for any little grey creepy crawlies or clutches of white eggs as this would indicate a parasite problem. The outer feathers should be glossy and shine.

Finally, check the production end. The vent should be clean with soft fluffy down feathers around it; these should not be contaminated with any droppings.

If you are happy with your girls, head home as soon as possible (after paying for them, of course).

How do I get my chickens home?

If you have arranged to view some chickens with the consideration of taking them home with you, then it would be advisable to be prepared and have a suitable box or carrier to transport them home in, as you will not be able to sit them on your lap in the car on the way home.

If you have a plastic pet carrier, the type used to take the cat to the vet, that would be perfect, however it's not cost effective to buy one to get your girls home. There are many cardboard types on the market or use a large, strong cardboard box with plenty of holes (at least 25mm) cut near the top to allow the hot air to escape and give maximum air flow. It would be kinder for the girls and your passengers to drive with the windows open. Please do not stop on the way home to get supplies as a locked car will get hot extremely quickly. If you have a long journey please stop en-route to check on the girls, but don't open their carrier at this stage otherwise you may be chasing chickens down the motorway.

What do I do when I get the girls home?

The next 24 hours will be one of the most stressful times of your chicken's life (unless it meets up with the local fox). Ideally, if you are able to purchase your girls as late in the day as possible, then put them straight to bed; this will certainly reduce any stress levels. If it is earlier in the day and assuming that the coop is fully prepared, and food and water is inside, then the girls can go straight inside. If the run is small then leave the pop hole open so they can have a look around. Please do not introduce them to the children or other pets on this first day as it can be a bit too much. A little Poultry Tonic in their water will help reduce the stress levels or even a very small piece of toast with Marmite on.

Next morning they can be let out at the crack of dawn and enjoy their new surroundings. To keep your girls friendly it's worth picking them up and giving them a stroke morning and evening for just 20 seconds each time during the first week. You will be amazed how they respond; after the first week they will be following you around like lambs!

Why are they not laying?

Eggs do not simply appear; there are many factors to consider. The most important requirement is the correct dietary needs. If your girls are not laying for any reason simply remove all tit-bits and confine them to a small area for a few days, giving them access to only Layers pellets, making sure there is a fresh water supply nearby. This should then get them back on track to laying more eggs.

If the girls have had a fright (such as meeting an unfriendly dog or fox), this could put them off lay for up to six weeks. If you add Poultry Tonic to their water this will help to return the vital vitamins and minerals back into them. One thing to bear in mind is it's not only you who enjoys eating the eggs that your girls have laid. If you are not quick enough to pick up those eggs in the morning, jackdaws, magpies, rodents and even dogs might steal them.

Moulting is a natural process but it is worth remembering that it can also be brought on by other factors such as stress or dehydration and, in some extreme cases, sudden weather changes.

Moulting

After continuously pumping out eggs for 15 months or so, the body naturally drains and needs recharging so they go into a moult. At this point they look as though they are going through a bad hair day with feathers falling out and looking lethargic. Depending on the time of year this moult can last up to eight weeks. The moult can happen at any time of the year, depending on when they were hatched. Losing your winter coat in January can come as quite a shock. When this happens the girls need a little TLC to help them pull through. Encourage them to eat as much as possible and add some Poultry Tonic into the water to help replenish the vitamins that have drained away during this process.

Whilst moulting, the calcium levels drain from the body, therefore egg production ceases or drops drastically. Nature takes its own course and once the whole process has finished she will come back into lay again. It is vital that protein levels are kept high during a moult as the feather regrowth relies entirely on protein content. It is for this reason that this is one time that you can spoil your girls with a handful of mealworms each day, or change their diet to Chick Crumbs (not to be fed to laying birds, though).

Indications of a moult are the comb and wattles lose their reddish colour and turn very light pink, the feathers around the neck will slowly drop out, and you will notice her tugging away at the feathers, trying encourage the new feathers to come through. The long primary feathers on the wings are normally the first to fall out; she will become grumpy and possibly go off her food. Please bear in mind that with all this going on her entire body will be very sore and tender so she will not appreciate being picked up and cuddled!

Predators

We all know that the fox is just waiting outside the gate each night in hope that you forgot to lock your girls away, but please remember that he is not the only creature after a free dinner; dogs are the largest killers of poultry in the domestic setting. I have had more phone calls telling me that the neighbours' dogs have just killed the pet chickens than anything else. It's for that reason that the perimeter fencing should be secure. Badgers are stronger than foxes. Despite not being able to scale tall fences, they are quite capable of using their powerful jaws to destroy any loose wire. Birds of prey can be a problem in rural areas, but as long as the girls have some form of cover in their runs this should be enough. Rooks, jackdaws and crows will also attack the smaller birds and they enjoy an uncooked omelette and seem to have a competition on how many eggs they can steal. Mink and stoats, as well all other rodents, are attracted to any kind of poultry, however with good housekeeping these horrid things can be kept at bay. Making sure that your feed supply is stored in a suitable container and that scraps are removed from the chicken run floor each night will minimise the risk.

Secure housing and well-designed fencing will also reduce the risk of these predators savaging your pets. If you have an enclosed run, secure a sheet of weld mesh on to the base and 45cm beyond the perimeter, laying it on to the grass. Within weeks the grass will grow through, giving it strong support against the fox or any other animal trying to dig into the run, as they always will try to dig at the edge (they are not normally clever enough to think of digging half a metre away).

There are many suggestions on how to keep the fox away: hanging human hair in bags around the chicken house, leaving a flashing light on or near the coop, putting lion's dung around the perimeter fences and even getting males to urinate alongside the house each night, but to be quite frank about the matter, if a fox is hungry he will find some way to get into your girls, so as long as you are happy with the security arrangements you have done your bit.

Persistent problems with a fox can only be solved by an expert shooter with a good rifle!

The dreaded red mite

I have more messages regarding red mite problems than anything regarding chicken welfare and it is one of those situations where prevention is better than cure. Those people who purchase plastic coops do not seem to have so many problems. However, red mites seem to come in from everywhere and they can lie dormant for years and then become a problem. Check the girls on a regular basis by gently moving their feathers upwards to see if you can see any grey (they remain grey until they have drawn blood from your girls) creepy crawlies scurrying through the down. If you see just one or two you have a problem. Another way of detecting a problem is to wait until it is dark and put your hand inside the nest box; hold it there for 30 seconds and you will soon know how it feels to be invaded by them, as they will crawl up your arm! Laying double-sided sticky tape or fly-paper on the top of the house will also help you to spot them. If your girls refuse to go to bed at night by just waiting at the door and refusing to go inside then there is a high possibility that there is a problem inside the house. Chickens that are lethargic and hunched should be checked, as eventually these little mites will suck so much out of the girls that they will die.

Prevention is, without any doubt, better and easier than cure. A few good housekeeping tasks will keep these little urchins away.

- Pay particular attention to the perches and underneath the feeders and drinkers.
- Clean out the house on a regular basis, keeping a beady eye out for any signs of a red mite presence.
- Keep any soiled bedding well away from the house otherwise they will soon be creeping back home again.
- Check your girls on a regular basis; this also keeps them friendly.
- Scatter Diatom around the inside of the house weekly. This is an organic product and, as the mites crawl to attack their prey, the dust cuts them, which eventually causes them to disintegrate.
- Wash out the house on a regular basis using a solution of strong poultry disinfectant, preferably one that melts the eggs of the red mites. I have found that a product called Poultry Shield is the only product on the market that I know will melt the red mite eggs as well as killing off any live mites. All cracks and crevices should be sprayed into as this is where they will be hiding. Make sure that you follow the suggested dilution rates otherwise you will find it will not be as effective.
- Keep a regular watch on any bedding; buying this in sealed bags will reduce the risk of the little creatures breeding amongst it.

Dealing with an infestation is a tireless and heartbreaking task. If you feel that you are not getting anywhere fast, you might read on a forum that the only cure is to burn the house down! Of course, this will work, but it is rather drastic. Perseverance is the main requirement. The mites will be laying eggs on a daily basis, with thousands hatching daily, so no matter how clever you are you are not going to destroy these in one swoop. Allow yourself 14 days minimum but do not be surprised if it takes twice that long to eradicate these dreaded creatures.

Clean out the coop every other day for 10 days, spraying Poultry Shield into

the roof space and any cracks on the sides and floor. Wash out the food and water bowls with Poultry Shield or a similar product at the same time, paying particular attention to the nest box area. Ideally, any spoilt bedding should be burnt; if that is not possible then store it in plastic bags and take it to your local dump.

Spray the chickens at the same time. I have found that Poultry Shield is ideal for this, however it does not carry a veterinary licence so you do so at your own peril. I have used it for the past 30 years with no adverse effects. There are some very good powders on the market that you can dust the affected girls with, or simply give the girls a good dusting with Diatom, but please watch their eyes and vents when using these products and do not forget to follow the Health & Safety guidelines for the user.

You will notice a reduction of activity in a few days, then after 10 days there will be only few stray ones. Do not stop the treatment then, simply go to once or twice a week, then you will see your girls perk up and very few mites to be seen. Mites can appear at any time of the year but most activity will take place during hot and damp seasons.

Other problems

Egg eating is one of those habits that infuriate the poultry keeper, and also a habit that is hard to break. I have tried so many ways of solving the problem. Once I even filled up a blown egg with my favourite brand of whiskey, but to my sheer horror found all the chickens liked the taste of it as they ran merrily around the paddock.

Again, there are many remedies to prevent the girls eating their own eggs but I could not guarantee which ones will be the most effective. Filling a blown egg with a very strong mustard mix probably gives the most amusing results, or a product called Stop Peck (I have found this one useful in stopping my granddaughter biting her nails and puppies chewing the furniture – however, these are not official tips) sprayed on the outside of the egg.

China or plastic eggs sometimes work, but the most reliable method is to keep the nest box as dark as possible using a dark cloth across the front with a slit to allow access, as chickens cannot see in the dark. This prevents them from seeing the eggs and therefore stops them from pecking at them.

Egg abnormalities may be a sign of problems. Eggs come in all shapes and sizes and there can be a variation in colours as well. As long as the egg is not too large or soft your girls will pop them out quite happily. It's when they start becoming too large or misshaped that you should worry.

Soft-shelled eggs, and ones that have calcium deposits on them, may indicate compacted crop. For years now the use of grit has been promoted to increase the bird's ability to break down the feed as it goes through her digestive system. Unfortunately the hybrid girls have a smaller crop capacity and find when they consume large amounts of grit it lodges in the gullet and sometimes can cause compacted crop.

I do not like feeding any form of grit on an ad-lib basis. If you are able to mix up a handful of grit into their feed you will find they will be able to digest this easier. We have found the use of products containing higher amounts of calcium and other vitamins put into the girls' water periodically helps to maintain strong and healthy egg shells and reduces egg abnormalities.

Prolapse in chickens is not a pretty sight and it's not very pleasant for the young lady, either. This can be caused by several different reasons. Too large an egg being passed is most common before she goes into a moult or, as she gets older, when the muscles get weaker. Soft-shelled eggs are extremely difficult for them to pass and therefore the oviduct is stretched. Normally the oviduct retracts, however where it is strained with the forcing of the large or soft-shelled egg, the whole oviduct remains on the outside of the poor chicken, which is soon noticeable even to the novice keeper.

Prevention is simply making sure that your girls have a well-balanced diet with adequate calcium levels, and they have plenty of exercise and access to sunshine. This should help to keep the girls healthy enough to prevent it happening. However, as long as your girls are laying, there will be a chance that they are going to have a prolapse, and without me sounding too much of a callous farmer, I would say that it's less than a 50% chance that you will get the prolapse to stay back in. Some vets will stitch it back but once the chickens commence laying it will more than likely pop out again.

Treatment can be carried out by a novice as long as you are prepared to get your hands dirty!

Prepare yourself with plastic gloves, some Witch Hazel and some warm soapy water. Remove your patient from the flock and have an area to put her into after you have treated her, otherwise the rest of the flock will peck at her, causing major problems.

Wash the entire area with the soapy water, taking care not to damage the delicate tissue and making sure that the entire oviduct is clear of any droppings and damaged egg. Once you are satisfied that it is clean enough, gently dry the protruding parts and dab Witch Hazel all over. Then, with two fingers, gently push the prolapse back in and hold there for 30 seconds or so. She will naturally try to resist. Be prepared to see it pop out again within minutes, so repeat the process if this happens or seek veterinary assistance.

If it stays in at this point keep her isolated from the rest of the flock, monitoring her on a regular basis. Do not put her back with the others until she has healed up completely.

Please do not be tempted to strap her up to prevent the prolapse as this can cause the girls a great deal of discomfort. There are different types on the market, fine for the poultry fanciers, but definately not for the domestic keeper.

Eye problems are quite common with chickens, which is not surprising when you consider where their heads are half of their lives, facing downwards with dust and all sorts flying in all directions.

Despite the eyelids moving upwards she is bound to catch a few flying objects in the eye. When this happens there is a chance of scratches within the eye housing. A warm tea bag applied on this twice a day normally helps to relieve this, or if the problem persists then an eye balm (make sure it's a veterinary one) will sort out the problem.

If the eye is weeping and there is a discharge from the nostril, we are looking at a different problem. This could be the start of a cold or even mycoplasma. If you find more than one chicken with these symptoms, then you will require some assistance.

If you look through the website forums, please be careful not to get too carried away with what you read, otherwise a common cold could turn into avian flu. It's always best to seek the advice of people who deal with poultry on a regular basis, preferably the person that you purchased them from.

Respiratory diseases identified in early stages will not be a problem; it is when they are not treated that they become fatal. Just a quick look at the girls' nostrils each morning will soon tell you if your girls are unwell. Sometimes a grass seed can cause them to have a sneezing fit. This can go on for several days, but a damp piece of cotton wool wiped across the nostril on each side will normally dislodge any foreign bodies hiding there. If she is lethargic and has a bubbly type mucus forming at the nostrils and her eyes are swollen with bubbles forming, there is something more sinister going on, most likely mycoplasma.

Hold her close to your ear and listen to her breathing; if it sounds rattly (like some one who smokes 30 cigarettes a day) she needs to be treated. Antibiotics do not kill viruses, however they will sort out a bacterial infection, which is normally brought on as a secondary infection. The choice is yours: you could take her to a vet to seek advice or increase her vitamin levels by introducing a Poultry Tonic into their water (it is best to treat all the girls). There could be various problems at this stage. Please do not worry yourself by looking up all the different viruses with long names. In the domestic flock it's best to simply seek your veterinary surgeon's advice; this is when you need the list of vaccines that you requested when you purchased them.

Scaly legs is where small mites burrow into the girls' legs, forcing the scales to raise, which in turn dry out and become crusty. It is very irritable for the girls, as you can imagine. The old-fashioned way of treating this is to stand the girls in a jar of surgical spirit at least once a week. It will take months to get rid of them. Gently rubbing Vaseline or Diprobase on to the affected areas will help to suffocate the mites; it will also aid recovery of the skin and scales. There are various products on the market which can be sprayed onto their legs on a regular basis, which seem just as efficient, and certainly not so brutal, as surgical spirit.

Cramp is not uncommon in chickens. It you find your girls struggling to walk and dragging a leg, it highly likely that she has cramp. It is more common in damp conditions. If you soak their leg under very warm water, two or three times a day, stretching the leg as much as possible, you will normally sort out the problem within a few days. Should the problem persist then it could be a damaged ligament or tendon. Generally, if she is not weight bearing then veterinary advice should be sought. However, if she is just hobbling around then time is normally the best healer.

Worms are present in most poultry, however they are not always a problem and they can live together in perfect harmony. If your chicken gets stressed then that is when the worms can take over. There are many types of worms working inside the girl's digestive system. Some can even take over inside the respiratory system. The common sign of an affected bird is white droppings sticking to the down feathers around the vent. I, personally, would not sell a bird unless it had been wormed with Flubenvet as I know the risk of sending a chicken to a new home, maybe mixing with other chickens, can cause major problems. On the other hand, if I only had two or three chickens producing eggs for us to eat, then I would be reluctant to use an active wormer. Of course, if the chickens were showing symptoms of a worm infestation then they should be dosed immediately. My choice of action would be to add Diatom into the girls' feed on a regular basis. This will certainly help to keep the worm levels down, but it is not a registered pesticide so the manufacturer does not promote it as a method of control. It definitely will not eliminate them but I would be happier eating the eggs. Using a clove of garlic in the water not only helps to build up a strong immune system, it does reduce the worm population in chickens as well. That's one that I learnt from my mother many years ago, and it's still just as effective (and, no, you will not get garlic tasting eggs for breakfast). My preferred option is to send off a dung sample to a specialist company found online to identify whether there is a worm problem in your flock; this has become an economical practice both for the domestic keeper and the commercial ones, too.

Egg peritonitis is a problem found in some older chickens, which lay unformed eggs and the yolk drops off into the egg tract; sometimes this can be absorbed, however if this problem persists then you will find your girl walking like a penguin and with an expanded undercarriage. If you catch this soon enough a course of antibiotics prescribed by the vet would give her a better chance of survival. However, you may decide it would it be kinder to put her down.

Compacted crop can cause a great deal of discomfort to your girls. It normally affects the greedy ones amongst them as they dive into the feed like they have never been fed before. The crop only allows a certain amount of food through at a time, to allow the enzymes time to work. That is why the girls normally go to bed in the evening and as they sleep the food gradually filters through. If, in the morning, she still has full crop then that is the first indications of a problem brewing. For them, it's a form of indigestion. Olive oil is still the best form of treatment for this problem. If you feel that your chicken is suffering with a compacted crop simply offer her some olive oil mixed in a small tomato, as this will help dislodge the blockage. If she doesn't take this on her own, then syringe some down her throat, very slowly, through the side of the beak, three or four times a day. If you are not squeamish, and the patient is still eating, offer her some white maggots (must be white). These are available from a fishing shop or online. These little creatures will take four days or so to eat their way

through the debris in the crop. If the blockage is not cleared in a few days this will then lead to a sour crop, which has the same symptoms but when you open the chicken's beak you will experience an awful smell. This demands urgent and drastic action. Tipping the girl downwards, keeping her beak well away from you, massage the crop until fluid comes out. Do this for a maximum of 20 seconds as the poor girl cannot breathe efficiently whist this is happening. This will need to be done at least four times a day before any results are seen. Please bear in mind that you are only trying to remove the fluid from her and not the solids, otherwise choking can prove fatal. If this fails then you will need to take her to your veterinary surgeon, who will be able to lance the crop, which despite being very expensive is not always successful.

The best way of preventing compacted crop from happening in the first place is not to use hay in the nest boxes as they tend to try to eat this (barley straw is fine), and reduce access to grass areas in the spring as they gouge themselves on this. It may help to not let your girls out of their house until mid morning. Yes, they will complain, but at least by the time they go out to eat they will have a full crop, which reduces the risk of them over-indulging. Keep the feeders off the ground so they have to stretch their necks when eating their food, and make sure that there is adequate water near to their feeder as this aids digestion.

Feather pecking is quite common when introducing new girls together, mainly because they are territorial creatures and there will always be a pecking order in the poultry world. They sometimes will fight to the death and if that's not bad enough they will continue to eat the poor victim when they have killed her! Sometimes your older girls will set on each other for no apparent reason, after living in harmony for years. This can be brought on by several different reasons: boredom, dietary changes or simply a fall out within the flock. Very often a moult is mistaken for a pecking problem, so it's important that a close examination of the feathers is carried out before telling your girls off. You will notice broken feathers under the larger remaining ones; these are normally surrounded by peck marks on the skin. If the problem is obvious, and you witness it happening, it is most likely the bird with the largest comb that is the bully. The quickest and most effective way of dealing with it is to find a powerful hosepipe and hide behind the coop and when the offending bird picks on its prey give it a quick, short blast behind the head. The trick is not to let it know it's you behind the hosepipe; she needs to believe that the victim has a friend up in the sky! Please do not allow children to take on this role, otherwise you might have drowned chickens. I admit it does sound cruel but certainly not so cruel as being pecked to death. If the birds are losing feathers and flesh is showing it's best to shake some talcum powder or mite powder over them to give them all a neutral smell. Various products can be purchased to spray on the girls to prevent them pecking, however I have found that vinegar mixed with water is just as efficient. If blood is drawn then an ultraviolet antiseptic spray should be put on the wound as it will help the healing process and cover up any signs of blood. As a rule of thumb, if the victim is being pecked at the top of the head or if she is bleeding then she should be removed. Better still, if you know who the bully is, put that one into confinement. You might have read that putting vinegar in their water will stop pecking if it's a dietary problem, however, it would make much more sense to put in a vitamin balancer such as a Poultry Tonic, which is processed to supply the chicken with all the vitamins required.

Who do I turn to when my chicken is ill?

Like any pet there will be a day when your girls become ill and you need some advice. The first answer is to pick up the phone or email the person who supplied your girls to you. Not all poultry sellers offer a back-up service and some offer only a limited warranty on the birds, but it is always worth trying in the first instance. At Longdown Activity Farm we pride ourselves for giving unlimited advice to people who have purchased their girls from us, and we are happy to discuss problems with other poultry keepers. We are not vets but we have years of practical experience in looking after chickens. If the illness is severe we will recommend a veterinary practice that has experience with poultry and is close to you.

Harvesting your eggs

It doesn't matter how many chickens you have in your flock, the main reason they are being kept is to supply you and your family with eggs to eat. Of course, some poultry keepers insist that they are part of the family and even if they didn't produce eggs they would still be happy to feed them. At this point I will admit that I probably have more chickens in my flock that I am paying their pension than that I have paying their way in eggs! Even though I am a farmer, I admit I can be a bit soft when it comes to culling a healthy bird.

It is vital that you harvest the eggs on a daily basis. One of the enjoyments of keeping your own girls is to be able to know exactly how fresh your eggs are. Also, if you leave the eggs in the nest box for a few days, you will be enticing little predators to come and steal them.

There is a lot of discussion on how an egg should be stored. I like the egg skelter system where you put the eggs into the skelter and they roll gently down so you know the one at the bottom is the oldest. Some people insist that all eggs should be refrigerated, which is true if your kitchen or larder is going to exceed 22 degrees Celsius; otherwise, room temperature is fine.

If your girls are kept in clean conditions then it is unlikely that there will be any salmonella or e-coli on the eggs, therefore why put them into a chilled environment where they are more likely to become contaminated or tainted with the other food stored next to them.

Should the egg be stored with the pointed end upwards or facing down? Everyone is going to have an opinion on this, with some very valid reasons. My personal belief is to eat the eggs as soon as possible, then you won't have to worry about how they are stored. Eggs can be stored for up to four weeks, however we are keeping our girls to provide us with fresh eggs so let's eat them as soon as we possibly can. More omelettes and cakes for me, please!

Chickens as a business

Starting an egg production business can teach youngsters how to manage money as well as taking responsibility for looking after animals. We have helped numerous budding entrepreneurs to take on the role of chicken keepers. Normally the parents or grandparents purchase all the equipment as a Christmas or birthday present; sometimes a redundant shed in the garden is allocated. The youngsters then have the task of finding out how to look after their new pets. Once you mention earning money, their ears prick up and they are determined to get started. When the new flock arrives it's almost instant cash as they charge their parents, friends and family as well as the neighbours ridiculous amounts of money for half a dozen eggs. Much better and safer than a paper round!

If you are considering helping a youngster (or an adult) take on a venture like this it is important that it is discussed in full prior to any purchases as this is a very large commitment and you are dealing with livestock. I normally suggest that a business plan should be drawn up; you would be surprised on how well a 10-year-old can put such a plan together with the help of an adult.

1) The plan should include discussing whom the eggs are to be sold to, ensuring there is a market out there: maybe this is to families, neighbours and schoolmates' parents. At this stage it would be worth while the young potential keeper making some enquiries; this will give them confidence

in communicating with adults. It would be advisable to mention to the neighbours that you are considering keeping chickens in the garden. Be prepared for some negative comments and be ready to reassure them that you will not have a noisy cockeral, and that you will prevent them straying into their garden. Likewise, you will do your utmost to prevent rodents becoming a problem.

2) Where will the chickens be kept? I know some grandparents encourage the grandchildren to keep them at their house. This is a sneaky way to see the grandchildren more often, but this is when it must be stressed to the budding farmer that animals have to be looked after. This means going to the chicken coop in the morning before school and putting the girls to bed seven days a week. Do not give any slight indication that you may be able to do it for them, otherwise guess who will be doing all the mucking out, and who will be reaping the rewards.

3) How much will the coop and equipment cost and how are they going to raise this capital cost? You will be surprised how smart and persuasive these youngsters are. They will have no hesitation in phoning aunts and uncles and tracking down relatives that you haven't seen for years, suggesting that they give them cash for their birthday or Christmas. They will find the funding, don't you worry, and they know that you will top up any shortcomings, anyway!

4) A daily routine will need to be organised: feeding, watering and harvesting the eggs. I also encourage them to keep a record of the number of eggs collected each day, and numbers damaged. This will help to make them realise that it is not all profit. I would warn them that there could be a few fatalities along the way so they need to build this into their plan.

4) Budget, so they have an idea of outgoing and incoming costs. This is a very simple way to encourage them to think ahead. As the business grows they will need to decide if they wish to earn more money or re-invest the money to expand the business.

5) Keep details of income received and how much has been spent on food

and bedding. Of course, they will not be treating the family to a holiday in Barbados on their profit but even if they only break even they will have gained from it in terms of animal welfare, communicating with friends and family, and, most of all, the value of money. All this can be achieved by keeping a few chickens in the garden, occupying about two hours of their time each week.

If they are still interested in becoming a mini poultry farmer I strongly suggest that you take them to a local chicken supplier armed with lots of questions. It may be best to arrange an appointment first, and discuss all the requirements with them before actually purchasing anything. Then, if everyone has not been put off, put the plan into action.

Can you keep other animals with chickens?

Some poultry keepers do keep rabbits and Guinea pigs in the same area as chickens. This is something that I would not recommend as rabbits can carry various diseases that are transmittable to poultry, likewise chickens can be carriers of viruses that can affect the rabbits and Guinea pigs. If you decide that you wish to create a farmyard environment and have them all together in an outdoor run, please make sure that they do have separate living accommodation that they can go to when it's bedtime. Chickens do go to sleep at night whilst the four-legged creatures like to stay awake and keep everyone else awake as well. Likewise, ducks and chickens will mix together in the foraging area, but at bedtime the chickens sitting on the roost above the poor ducks will deliberately bombard them with the ten poos that they eject each night, so please make sure that the ducks have a cosy area where they can go to sleep away from the chickens. I'm also concerned about the amount of ammonia that the ducks create during the night. This will travel upwards where the chickens are perched, which can cause some major respiratory problems.

What to do with the supply of eggs

There are so many ways that you can enjoy the eggs that the girls produce. I know of one lady who doesn't eat a single egg that her chickens provide. She tells me that she simply couldn't eat them so she decorates all of them and then sells them at a local craft stall. That's not for me! I really do enjoy tucking into the largest omelette that I can fit onto my plate, mixed with as many garnishes that I can find. Eggs are good for children to experiment their cooking skills with but bear in mind that there is a slight possibility that salmonella is lurking underneath the shell so it is vital that they are cooked properly.

The favourite of most children is a boiled egg with some toasted soldiers. It is a good idea to get the children to try a different type of egg recipe each day of the week. I suggest this to schools that visit us and many teachers are amazed at how creative the children can be.

When your chicken's had her chips

Chickens do not live forever. Unfortunately the girls will eventually die or, harder still, will need to be put down (most hybrids will live four to five years). As most domestic keepers become very attached to their girls it is very difficult when a decision has to be made to put them down. Some people will not have a problem with putting their pet to sleep, as at least it will no longer be suffering. Others will need assistance. Again it would be worth a phone call to your supplier or veterinary surgeon, or, if you know someone who keeps ferrets, they may be happy to help. As the law stands it is illegal for your chicken to be buried on your premises as poultry do not come under the pet exemption category, therefore it is suggested that you take your chicken's body to a veterinary surgeon or somewhere else registered to dispose of animal carcases.

I don't advocate going against the law but if you do decide to bury your girl in the garden please bury it in a deep hole (at least a metre) and cover it with lime or a strong disinfectant to avoid foxes and badgers digging it up.

It's always worth contacting your local Trading Standards office as it's their responsibility to govern the disposal of livestock.

In Conclusion

I sincerely hope that reading this book has not put you off keeping chickens and that you have many years of fun and entertainment looking after your girls.

I have attempted to give the reader a realistic insight of keeping chickens. Of course, there will be a few problems to overcome on the journey, but the contents of this chicken manual should help you identify any problems and, in most cases, help to rectify them.

There are lots of forums and Facebook pages handing out advice on how to keep your chickens, however your first port of call should be from the person that you purchased them from, or you are welcome to join my Facebook page 'Longdown pets and poultry' or subscribe to my monthly newsletter 'enquiries@ longdownfarm.co.uk'.

I assure you that you will be rewarded with plenty of tasty eggs and hours of entertainment. All they ask from you is just a little TLC and plenty of food. You will never wish to eat a supermarket egg again.

Index

Also Available

Bryan Pass is also the author of several children's books, also available from Ceratopia Books, and illustrated by Simon Chadwick:

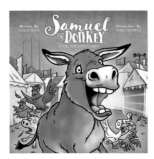

Samuel The Donkey
ISBN: 9780954279165
Price: £4.99

Fudge The Jersey Cow
ISBN: 9780954279172
Price: £4.99

Doris The Chicken
ISBN: 9780954279189
Price: £4.99

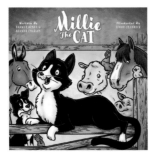

Millie The Cat
ISBN: 9780954279196
Price: £4.99

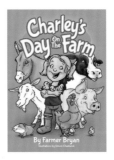

Charley's Day On The Farm
ISBN: 9780954279110
Price: £4.99

All books are available from **www.ceratopiabooks.co.uk**